box cars and one-eyed jacks™

VOLUME III

SPECIAL GAMES
with
SPECIAL DICE

Written by:

Joanne Currah
Jane Felling
Cheryl MacDonald

"Box Cars" won the National Learning Disabilities Association Idea of the Year 1991.

© 1992 BOX CARS & ONE-EYED JACKS™
ISBN: 0-9695276-2-4

ACKNOWLEDGEMENT

To all the terrific kids across the country
who have enthusiastically played our games.

" Dear Joanne, Jane & Cheryl,

Thanks for coming to our school. I liked the dice with all different sides and the games you taught us. You should write another book of games. I would like that. **"**

Yours truly,
R.M.
Grade 4

TABLE OF CONTENTS

"Dear Joanne, Jane & Cheryl,

I really appreciated you guys coming in and teaching us different games. My favorite part was when you showed us different games. I learned that math can be fun! I think other kids would like to learn more of your games. I think you showed math work too, because we played multiplication games. Your presentation was very enjoyable and educational. **"**

Yours truly,
A.B.
Grade 4

INTRODUCTION

SPECIAL GAMES WITH SPECIAL DICE was created for the sole purpose of making math fun for children. Much of the skill and drill activities that young children are faced with daily, have had just the opposite effect.

The child-centered games included were created for use in the regular and special needs classroom, as well as in the home. They have been designed to take the boredom and frustration out of the repetitive practice necessary for children to master important math skills and concepts. The games format allows adults to observe and evaluate the thinking strategies and problem solving strategies the children are using.

Children are normally eager to play games. When presented in an exciting format, children will concentrate and repeat them over and over again. This repetition is the key to mastery. In a non-threatening game format, children will be more focused and retention will be greater. In a game situation children do not suffer the RED X for making a mistake, as they so often do when doing exercises in a workbook. This helps foster a positive self-esteem and attitude towards math.

The games included in this book create situations where children have opportunities to discover math concepts. The learning is self and peer directed. The games can be adapted to serve both remedial and enrichment programs. Children learn from each other and through manipulating the materials. Varied ability groupings are presented in games to allow for the greatest interaction possible.

It is our hope that children will find that math can be fun, not threatening or frustrating. For teachers or parents who need another way to help, we hope our games offer part of the answer. Let yourself go, and get into the spirit of SPECIAL GAMES WITH SPECIAL DICE. You'll find yourself having as much fun as the children.

HOW TO USE THIS BOOK

SPECIAL GAMES with SPECIAL DICE contains 50 games. The games are organized sequentially from the easiest to the most difficult level. Each game is presented in the following format:

SKILLS: specific math skills are listed.

PLAYERS: number needed for playing - intended to be flexible. You may want to change rules to add or subtract players. Many games can be played as solitaire.

EQUIPMENT: specific items are listed, including type of dice needed. Counters, paper and pencil should always be made available. All games require either 10-, 12- or 20-sided dice.

GETTING STARTED: rules and instructions which can be changed to meet individual and class needs.

VARIATIONS: ideas to increase or decrease difficulty, or to change skill focus.

The games do not have to be played in a set order. Teachers and parents can select games to:

1. introduce a concept or skill
2. practice a concept or skill
3. master a concept or skill

Many of the games build on each other. However, they do not need to be taught in sequence. Make sure to double check the Skills section before starting. The rules and instructions are flexible. You can change the equipment, rules, or how to determine the winner, to focus on different abilities and/or skills, competitive/non-competitive format.

Many of the games rely on luck to determine the eventual winner of the game. Children will learn that winning is not always the most important aspect of the game. Repetitive practice of skills are central to each and every game. It is the key element that makes these games practical for use in the school and home.

Organization

Games were a part of every lesson. We allowed anywhere from ten to twenty minutes for math games every day. As well, children could play math games during free time/center time. It is important that play and practice time be consistent for all students. The games were not used as rewards and all students played. Usually students were given a choice of games and selected one that was the most appropriate. Pairs and groups were selected initially by the teacher. This ensures appropriate groupings. Pairings and groupings were changed frequently.

The games were usually taught to the entire group first. The class usually played the game for a number of days until it was well understood. After a number of games had been taught on a single concept, students or teacher would choose the one that was most appropriate for them to play. During a typical games period many different games can be played.

Teachers may wish their students to have a permanent record of the games period. Some teachers have students record some of their work in a permanent place such as a BOX CARS BOOK. A listing of the games played, strategies used, and skills to work on may be recorded.

Encourage children to play the games at home for extra practice. We often included a game in our newsletters home to parents. During parent-teacher interviews, when parents ask what they can do to help their children at home, have some game instructions available. Games are also useful activities to leave for a substitute teacher.

Box Cars games should complement your existing math program, not replace it. It is in this spirit we hope that SPECIAL GAMES with SPECIAL DICE will be helpful to teachers and parents in meeting the needs of their children.

Finally, HAVE FUN!

– Joanne, Jane and Cheryl

* If more special dice are required see back page for ordering information.

ODD AND EVEN

SKILLS: number recognition, odd/even

PLAYERS: 2 - 4

EQUIPMENT: 1 twelve-sided die, 100 "cube-a-links" (minimum); two colors – 50 of each (one color to represent even numbers, and one color to represent odd numbers)

GETTING STARTED: Player one rolls the die and determines whether the number is even or odd. If even, the player takes the appropriate number of even colored cubes and links these together. If odd, they take the appropriate number of odd colored cubes. Player two takes a turn. Players continue alternating turns each building two separate rows of cubes (one to represent an even row and one to represent an odd row). After ten rolls players compare their odd and even trains. The longest trains score a point.

VARIATION: Have players build two trains of 50 (one with each colour). Players roll and subtract from their odd and even trains. The first players to shrink their trains score a point.

9

A DETECTIVE'S ROLL

SKILLS: place value, odd/even, betweenness

PLAYERS: Groups of 4-6

EQUIPMENT: One twenty-sided die per player

GETTING STARTED: A "detective" is chosen for the group. The detective's job is to determine the value of each player's roll. Players secretly roll their die. The detective then gives the following instructions: "All players who rolled 10 or less sit down." This becomes the detective's first clue. The detective then selects a player for "questioning." The detective is allowed two questions per player. Examples: "Is you number odd or even?" or "Is your number between 15 and 20?". The detective must now guess that player's number. If correct, the detective scores one point. If not, the other player scores a point. The detective selects the next player and proceeds to guess their number. A new detective is selected after all players have been questioned. Play ends when all players have been the detective. The player with the most points wins.

VARIATION: Players roll two ten-sided dice and make a number between zero and ninety-nine. The detective is now allowed four to eight questions per player in attempt to guess the value of their roll.

ROLLING ALONG

SKILLS: number recognition, number matching

PLAYERS: 2 - 4

EQUIPMENT: 1 twelve-sided die, paper, pencil

GETTING STARTED: Each player makes a gameboard as follows: (see appendix for reproducible page)

1	2	3	4	5	6	7	8	9	10	11	12
		X	X	X							

The object is for each player to cross off all their numbers on their gameboard. Player one rolls the die and crosses off that same number on their gameboard. Player two then takes a turn. Players continue to alternate turns. If a player rolls a number that has already been crossed off, they earn a strike. Three strikes and a player is out and can not continue rolling. The game ends when all players are out, or one player gets all of their gameboard crossed off. If all players strike out, the player with the most numbers crossed off is the winner.

VARIATION: Use a 20-sided die and have a gameboard 1-20.

See page 18 for more advanced version.

COUNT 'EM AND EAT 'EM

SKILLS: 1 to 1 correspondence of numbers to 12, counting to 100

PLAYERS: 2 or more

EQUIPMENT: 1 twelve-sided die, bowl of cereal, "cube-a-links"

GETTING STARTED: Player one rolls the die and takes that number of "crunchies" from the bowl. Player two rolls the die and takes that number of crunchies. Players alternate until all players have had ten rolls. Players may need to keep track of how many rolls they have had. Each player could start with ten cubes linked together. At the beginning of each turn, the player breaks off one cube indicating they have one less turn to take. After each player has had ten turns, they may count up the total number of crunchies and eat them!

VARIATION: You could use a twenty-sided die and have the students count up to twenty, limit to 5 rolls.

ROLL IT AND MARK IT

SKILLS: number recognition, writing numerals, graphing

PLAYERS: 2 - 4

EQUIPMENT: 1 twelve-sided die, gameboard

GETTING STARTED: Each player has their own gameboard: (see appendix for reproducible page)

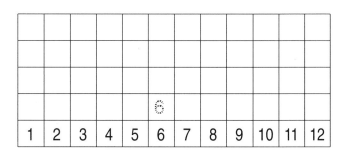

Player one rolls the die. Players must recognize the number on the die and write the corresponding numeral on their graph. Players alternate turns until one player has one horizontal row filled in. Encourage players to verbalize which number has been rolled the most, least, or same as another number.

EXAMPLE: A six is rolled, and the numeral six is recorded on their graph.

SKIP AWAY

SKILLS:	1 to 1 correspondence of numbers, counting to 200 patterned counting for beginning multiplication.
PLAYERS:	2 or more
EQUIPMENT:	1 twenty-sided die, "cube-a-links", paper, pencil
GETTING STARTED:	Player one rolls the die and takes that number of "cube-a-links" to link together. Players alternate rolling the die. Play continues until all players have had ten rolls. Players count up their cubes. The player with the most cubes is the winner. Players may need to keep track of how many rolls they have had. They may keep track tallying with paper and pencil. For multiplication, count each cube using 2's, 5's and 10's pattern or players may wish to count off 10's trains and use place value mats to determine their totals.

TAKE IT AWAY

SKILLS:	1 to 1 correspondence of numbers, counting, subtracting
PLAYERS:	2 - 4
EQUIPMENT:	K - 1: 1 twelve-sided die and 50 "cube-a-links" per player, container
	Grades 1 - 2: 1 twenty-sided die and 100 "cube-a-links" per player, container
GETTING STARTED:	To begin each player takes 50 or 100 cubes. Player one rolls the die and takes away that number of cubes from his 50 or 100 and places them in a container. Players alternate turns, taking away their cubes. The first player to have only one or no cubes left is the winner.
VARIATION:	Players may guesstimate how many rolls it will take to take away all of their cubes. They may share their guesses and see who was closest to their prediction. Players may use a graph to 12 to record their rolls.

SUBTRACT-A-GRAPH

SKILLS: subtraction facts to 12, writing numerals, beginning graphing

PLAYERS: 2 - 4

EQUIPMENT: 2 twelve-sided dice, gameboard, pencil

GETTING STARTED: Each player has their own gameboard: (see appendix for reproducible page)

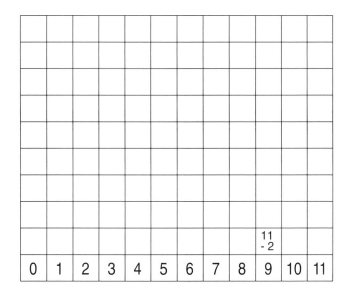

Player one rolls the dice and subtracts the smaller die from the larger die, then writes this equation in the appropriate space on their graph. For instance, if the roll is an 11 and a 2, the player determines the correct difference to be 9 and writes "11 - 2" in the 9 column of their graph. Players alternate turns until one player has one horizontal row filled in.

VARIATION: Have players work in pairs. Play for speed having pairs play against each other.

FAIR GAME ADDITION

SKILLS: adding to 40

PLAYERS: 2

EQUIPMENT: 4 twenty-sided dice, one 6-sided die

GETTING STARTED: Each player rolls two twenty-sided dice and adds them together. Player one rolls the six-sided die to determine who wins the point:

1, 3, 5 (odd) roll – lower sum wins the point.
2, 4, 6 (even) roll – higher sum wins the point.

Players continue to roll dice and add them together. Players alternate the roll of the six-sided die. If players roll equal sums, each player scores a point. The first player to score twenty points is the winner.

TIME OUT

SKILLS: telling time to the hour

PLAYERS: 1 or more

EQUIPMENT: 1 twelve-sided die, gameboard, paper, pencil

GETTING STARTED: Each player draws a clock with the minute hand drawn in (see appendix for reproducible page). Player one rolls the die and identifies the number rolled. This number becomes the hand the player may draw on their clock. Players take turns rolling and filling in the time on their own clock. The first player to complete their clock is the winner and calls "Time Out!"

VARIATION: Telling time to the half hour, quarter hour, and three quarter hour may also be worked on by changing the position of the hands on the clock.

Roll two twelve-sided dice and players may add or subtract them and cross out the time. i.e.; roll 6 and 5 may cross out 11 o'clock or 1 o'clock until only 12 remains. Players roll a single die until 12 is rolled.

SUB TRACK

Skills:	subtracting from twelve
Players:	2 - 4
Equipment:	2 twelve-sided dice, gameboard, pencil
Getting Started:	Each player draws a gameboard as follows: (see appendix for reproducible page)

0   1   2   3   4   5   6   7   8   9   10   11

X   X   X

Player one rolls the dice and subtracts the smaller die from the larger die and crosses off the answer on their gameboard. Player two then rolls the dice subtracts and crosses off the answer on their gameboard. Players continue to alternate turns. If a player is unable to cross off an answer, they earn a strike, circling the X. Three strikes and the player is out. Play continues until all players are out, or when one player crosses off all of the numbers on their gameboard. If all players strike out, the player with the most numbers crossed off is the winner.

WINNING TRACK CHALLENGER

SKILLS: adding, subtracting, multiplying, and dividing number combinations to 12

PLAYERS: 1 - 4

EQUIPMENT: 1 twelve-sided die, 1 ten-sided die, gameboard, paper

GETTING STARTED: Each player draws a gameboard as follows: (see appendix for reproducible page)

0   1   2   3   4   5   6   7   8   9   10   11   12

X   X   X

Player number one rolls both dice. Players may cross off up to three open numbers that, when combined, total up to that roll. For example, 8 and 2 are rolled. Player may now cross off any combinations that equal ten: $8 + 2$, $12 - 2$, 2×5, $10 - 0$, $0 + 4 + 6$, $(12 \div 3) + 6$, $11 - 1 - 0$, etc. Only one combination can be crossed off per turn. Player two may then take a turn. Players continue to alternate turns. If a player rolls a total that is impossible to cross off any number for, the player earns a strike, circling the X. Three strikes and a player is out and cannot continue rolling. The game ends when all players are out, or one player gets all numbers on their gameboard crossed off. If all players strike out, the player with the most numbers crossed off is the winner.

❝ Dear Joanne, Jane and Cheryl,

Thank you for coming to our school. I liked the dice, they were cool. And the game Winning Track Challenger was very fun. Do you like your books? My favourite dice were the Black ones. It went up to 31 didn't it? Are you coming to our school again? **❞**

yours truly,
B.F.
Grade four

SUM IT UP

SKILLS: adding of three digit numbers

PLAYERS: 2 - 4, or teacher vs. whole class

EQUIPMENT: 1 ten-sided die, paper, pencil

GETTING STARTED: One player will roll the die for the group. Each player makes a gameboard as follows:

$$\begin{array}{r} \underline{}\ \underline{}\ \underline{} \\ \underline{}\ \underline{}\ \underline{} \\ +\ \underline{}\ \underline{}\ \underline{} \\ \hline \end{array}$$

The goal of this game is to make the largest sum. The die is rolled. Each player puts the number into their gameboard (ie. If a two is rolled players could place the number in the one's place. If a nine were rolled, it would logically be placed in the hundred's place).

Player 1	Player 2	Player 3
__ 5 __	__ 8 __	9 __ __
9 __ __	9 __ 5	8 __ __
+ 8 __ 2	+ __ __ 2	+ __ 5 2

Each time the die is rolled the players decide where that number will go on their gameboard. After nine rolls, players add up their numbers. The player with the largest sum receives one point for the round. If more than one player gets the same sum, each player receives a point. For this round 2, 5, 9, 8, 1, 3, 4, 2, 6 were rolled and were placed into the grids by the players as follows:

Player 1	Player 2	Player 3
6 5 1	3 8 1	9 1 4
9 4 3	9 4 5	8 2 3
+ 8 2 2	+ 6 2 2	+ 6 5 2
2 4 1 6	1 9 4 8	2 3 8 9

Player number one scores the point, and can roll the next nine numbers.

VARIATION: Multiplication:

$$\begin{array}{r} \underline{}\ \underline{} \\ X\ \underline{}\ \underline{} \\ \hline \end{array} \qquad \text{OR} \qquad \begin{array}{r} \underline{}\ \underline{}\ \underline{} \\ X\ \underline{}\ \underline{}\ \underline{} \\ \hline \end{array}$$

FILL THE CARTON

SKILLS: subtracting from 12

PLAYERS: 2

EQUIPMENT: 4 twelve-sided dice, counters, numbered egg carton

GETTING STARTED: Each player has two twelve-sided dice, twelve counters and an egg carton. The goal of the game is to place a counter in each section of the numbered egg carton.

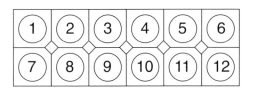

Player one rolls the dice and subtracts the smaller number from the larger determining the difference. The player then places a counter on this number in their egg carton. Player two rolls the dice and repeats the same procedure. To fill in number twelve, players must roll a double. Players continue until one player fills their carton.

VARIATION: 1. Players can add or subtract the dice.

2. Strike Outs – A player can get a strike if they roll a difference already filled in by a counter. Players can get up to three strikes, at which point they stop rolling. If both players strike out, the player with the most numbers filled is the winner.

SUBTRACTION SHAKEDOWN

SKILLS:	subtracting from 20
PLAYERS:	2
EQUIPMENT:	1 twenty-sided die per player, 1 twelve-sided die per player
GETTING STARTED:	Each player rolls their two dice and subtracts the smaller number from the larger number. The player with the smallest difference receives two points.

EXAMPLE:

Player 1	Player 2
18 - 9 = 9	14 - 3 = 11

Player one receives two points.

In the event of a tie (both players have the same difference), a tie breaker must be played. Each player rolls the dice again to get another difference. The first player to roll a difference less than the tie scores four points.

EXAMPLE:

Player 1	Player 2
16 - 8 = 8	17 - 9 = 8

Tie "8"

Tie Breaker

17 - 10 = 7	14 - 9 = 5

Player two receives four points because they have the smallest difference. Play continues until one player collects fifty points.

PLACE VALUE TOSS UP

SKILLS: place value to 100

PLAYERS: 2

EQUIPMENT: 2 ten-sided dice per player

GETTING STARTED: Each player rolls their two dice and makes the largest two-digit number possible and verbalizes it to their partner. The player with the largest number scores two points.

EXAMPLE:

Player 1	Player 2
6, 2 = 62	4, 3 = 43

Player one receives two points.

In the event of a tie (both players have the same number), a tie breaker must be played. Each player rolls the dice again to get another number between 1 - 100. The first player to roll a number higher than the tie scores four points.

EXAMPLE:

Player 1	Player 2
6, 9 = 69	6, 9 = 69

Tie "69"

Tie Breaker

3, 8 = 38	7, 6 = 76

Player two receives four points because they have the largest number. Play continues until one player scores fifty points.

SUBTRACTION SNAP

SKILLS: immediate recall, subtracting from 20

PLAYERS: 2 (equal skill level)

EQUIPMENT: 1 twenty-sided die, 1 ten-sided die

GETTING STARTED: At the same time, each player rolls one of the die. Players must subtract the smaller number from the larger number. The first player to say the correct answer out loud scores one point. In the event of a tie, no one scores a point. Play continues for a set period of time or until a certain number of points have been reached.

ADDITION SNAP

SKILLS: immediate recall of addition facts to 24

PLAYERS: 2 (equal skill level)

EQUIPMENT: 2 twelve-sided dice

GETTING STARTED: At the same time, each player rolls one of the die. Players must add the two numbers together. The first player who says the correct sum out loud scores one point. In the event of a tie, no one scores a point. Play continues for a set period of time or until a certain number of points have been reached.

TRIPLE SNAP

SKILLS: immediate recall of three addends, adding to 30

PLAYERS: 3 (equal skill level)

EQUIPMENT: 3 ten-sided dice

GETTING STARTED: At the same time, each player rolls one of the die. Players must add the three numbers rolled. The first player who says the correct sum out loud scores one point. In the event of a tie, no one scores a point. Play continues for a set period of time or until a certain number of points have been reached.

SNAP TO 40

SKILLS: immediate recall of addition facts to 40

PLAYERS: 2 (equal skill level)

EQUIPMENT: 2 twenty-sided dice

GETTING STARTED: At the same time, each player rolls one die. Players must add the two numbers together. The first player who says the correct sum out loud scores one point. In the event of a tie, no one scores a point. Play continues for a set period of time or until a certain number of points have been reached.

DOUBLE TROUBLE

SKILLS: adding doubles

PLAYERS: 2

EQUIPMENT: 2 ten-sided dice per player, paper, pencil

GETTING STARTED: Each player makes a gameboard as follows:

2   4   6   8   10   12   14   16   18

The goal of the game is to be the first player to cross all the numbers off their board. Players take turns rolling their dice in an attempt to roll doubles. If a double is rolled, the player finds the sum and crosses it off of their gameboard. Players each get three rolls per turn. The first player to cross off all of their numbers is the winner.

EXAMPLE: $4 + 4 = 8$ 8 is crossed off
                       $7 + 7 = 14$ 14 is crossed off

PUZZLING PLUSES

SKILLS: adding sums to 40

PLAYERS: 2

EQUIPMENT: 2 twenty-sided dice per player, paper, pencil

GETTING STARTED: Each player rolls two dice and adds the numbers together. The player with the greatest sum receives two points.

EXAMPLE:

Player 1	Player 2
4 + 9 = 13	7 + 9 = 16

Player two would win two points.

In the event of a tie (each player has the same sum), a tie breaker must be played. Each player rolls their dice again and finds the sum. The first player to roll a sum greater than the tie scores four points.

EXAMPLE:

Player 1	Player 2
7 + 3 = 10	5 + 5 = 10

Tie "10"

4 + 3 = 7	2 + 3 = 5

Neither sum higher than 10, roll again.

10 + 5 = 15	6 + 5 = 11

Player one receives four points for breaking the tie with the largest sum.

Play continues until one player scores fifty points.

PUZZLING CHALLENGES

SKILLS: addition, sums to 60

PLAYERS: 2

EQUIPMENT: 3 twenty-sided dice per player

GETTING STARTED: Each player rolls the dice and adds the numbers together. The player with the greatest sum receives two points.

EXAMPLE:

Player 1	**Player 2**
$13 + 7 + 3 = 23$	$12 + 3 + 10 = 25$

Player two wins two points.

In the event of a tie (each player has the same sum), a tie breaker must be played. Each player rolls their dice again and finds the sum. The first player to roll a sum greater than the tie scores four points.

EXAMPLE:

Player 1	**Player 2**
$4 + 13 + 5 = 22$	$7 + 9 + 6 = 22$

Tie "22"

$5 + 10 + 14 = 29$	$10 + 12 + 1 = 23$

Player one would win four points.

Play continues until one player wins fifty points.

METRE MADNESS

SKILLS: adding and subtracting to 100, odd and even numbers

PLAYERS: 2 - 4

EQUIPMENT: 1 ten-sided die, metre stick, coloured marker for each player

GETTING STARTED: Each player begins by placing their marker on the 50 cm mark of the metre stick. The goal is to be the first player to reach either 0 or 100. Each player in turn rolls the die. If the number is odd, the player subtracts and moves left (towards zero) on the metre stick that number. If the number is even, the player adds and moves that number to the right on the metre stick. The first player to land on 0 or 100 is the winner.

EXAMPLE: Player one rolls 8, records 50 + 8 = 58. Player one's second roll is 7, records 58 - 7 = 51, etc.

| 40 | 41 | 42 | 43 | 44 | 45 | 46 | 47 | 48 | 49 | 50 | 51 | 52 | 53 | 54 | 55 | 56 | 57 | 58 | 59 | 60 |

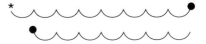

VARIATION: Have students record their rolls.

SOUNDS DICEY

SKILLS: addition, subtraction, odd / even

PLAYERS: 2

EQUIPMENT: 1 twenty-sided die, pencil, paper

GETTING STARTED: Each player starts with fifty points. Player one rolls the die. If the number is even, this number is added to their fifty points. If the number rolled is odd, this number is subtracted from their fifty points. Players continue rolling and continue to add or subtract from their accumulated points until one player reaches two hundred.

Note: If a player goes below zero, they freeze at zero until an even number is rolled.

EXPANDER

SKILLS: expanding numbers, adding to 10 000

PLAYERS: small groups, or teacher vs. whole class

EQUIPMENT: 1 twenty-sided die, pencil, paper

GETTING STARTED: The goal of the game is to create the largest number possible. The player(s) with the largest number score a point for that round. Groups can play to a set score (ie. 10 or 20 points) or for a set amount of time. Each player makes a grid as follows:

Thousands	Hundreds	Tens	Ones

A player from the group is selected to roll the twenty-sided die for the round. The die is rolled and each player must record that number somewhere on their grid. Once all players have filled in this number, the die is rolled again. This number is also placed in the grid. Two more rolls are taken to fill the grid, for a total of four rolls.

EXAMPLE: The four rolls are 12, 9, 6, 18

Player 1

Th	Hu	T	O
18	12	9	6

Player 2

Th	Hu	T	O
12	18	9	6

At the end of the four rolls, players total their rolls as follows:

Player 1
```
  18000
   1200
     90
+     6
  19296
```

Player 2
```
  12000
   1800
     90
+     6
  13896
```

Player one scores the point for the round.

If two or more players create the largest number they all score a point. Play continues until a player reaches a certain number of points or for a set period of time. The player with the most points wins.

Note: The more students play this game, the better their strategy will become.

VARIATION: Change grid to incorporate more place values:

Ten Thousands	Thousands	Hundreds	Tens	Ones

" Dear Joanne & Jane & Cheryl,

I liked Multiplication Golf.
I think the kids are going to like it. I learned the standard form of numbers. It helps me on math. **"**

J.H.
Grade 4

ROCK N' ROLL

SKILLS: creating a five-digit number

PLAYERS: 2 - 4

EQUIPMENT: 5 ten-sided dice per player

GETTING STARTED: All players roll their dice at the same time. Players then begin arranging their dice to make the largest five digit number possible. The first player to finish calls out "Rock N' Roll" and verbalizes their number to the other players. All other players must freeze their numbers in their current order, even if they are not finished arranging them.

If the first player done is also the player with the largest number of the group they score ten points. If not, they earn five points and the player who does have the highest number of the group would also earn five points. All other players earn zero. The first player to fifty is the winner.

WHAT'S MISSING?

SKILLS: identifying the missing addend

PLAYERS: 2

EQUIPMENT: 1 twenty-sided die, 1 ten-sided die, paper, pencil

GETTING STARTED: Player one rolls the ten-sided die and then rolls the twenty-sided die (ie. 3 and 17) and calls out the math sentence "$3 + \_ = 17$". Player two must determine what the missing addend is and call out the answer. If the answer is correct, the player receives one point. If the answer is incorrect, the other player can give their answer and if correct they earn a point. Players alternate turns. Play continues until one player reaches twenty points.

PEEK A BOO

SKILLS: identifying the missing addend

PLAYERS: 2

EQUIPMENT: 3 twelve-sided dice, margarine tub

GETTING STARTED: Player one secretly sets up an equation for player two. This is done by rolling one die and placing it on top of the margarine tub (1). A number on a second die that is greater than the die shown on the top of the tub is then chosen (2). Player one must determine the missing addend, and place the die with the number underneath the margarine tub (3). Player two can now look at the equation that player one has arranged. Player two must guess the missing addend by looking at the die on top of the tub and the die that is set aside and visible. They may then "peek" under the tub to see if their answer is correct. If so, players reverse roles. If the answer is incorrect, player one sets up a second equation. Players collect points each time the get a correct answer or when they stump an opponent.

EXAMPLE:

1.

2.

3.
5

Player could figure: 7 + ___ = 12

or: 12 −   7 = ___

or: 12 − ___ =   7

to get the answer.

PEEK A BOO RACE

SKILLS: identifying the missing addend, immediate recall

PLAYERS: 2 (equal skill level)

EQUIPMENT: 6 twelve-sided dice, margarine tub

GETTING STARTED: Follow the same game directions and rules as Peek A Boo, with the added variation of speed. Each player secretly sets up their own equation for their opponent. One player says "Go" and both players attempt to solve the other's equation at the same time. The first player to correctly solve their opponent's problem scores one point. The first player to score ten points is the winner.

NAME IT

SKILLS: identifying fractions, illustrating fractions

PLAYERS: 2

EQUIPMENT: 1 twelve-sided die, pencil, paper

GETTING STARTED: Player one rolls the die and names that number in a fraction (ie. rolls a six, names one-sixth). Player two must then draw a picture showing sixths.

EXAMPLE:

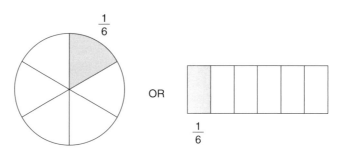

If the player correctly draws the corresponding fraction, they receive one point. Players alternate turns. The first player to score ten points is the winner.

FUN FRACTIONS

SKILLS:　　　　　　identifying proper fractions, illustrating fractions

PLAYERS:　　　　　2

EQUIPMENT:　　　　2 twelve-sided dice, pencil, paper

GETTING STARTED:　Player one rolls the two dice and uses these two numbers to create a proper fraction (ie. rolls a seven and a twelve; seven-twelfths). Player then draws the fraction.

EXAMPLE:

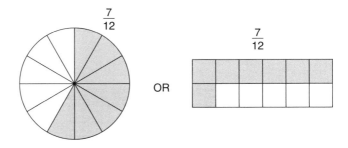

If the player draws the corresponding fraction correctly they receive one point. Players alternate turns. The first player to score ten points is the winner.

FAIR GAME MULTIPLICATION

SKILLS:　　　　　　multiplying to 100, odd and even numbers

PLAYERS:　　　　　2

EQUIPMENT:　　　　2 ten-sided dice per player, one six-sided die

GETTING STARTED:　Each player rolls their two ten-sided dice and multiplies them together. Player number one rolls the six-sided die to determine who wins the point.

1, 3, 5 - odd roll - lower product wins the point

2, 4, 6 - even roll - higher product wins the point

Players continue to roll the dice and multiply them. Players alternate the roll of the six-sided die. If the players roll equal products, each player receives a point. The first player to score twenty points is the winner.

MULTIPLICATION SNAP

SKILLS: immediate recall, multiplying to 100 / 144

PLAYERS: 2 (equal skill level)

EQUIPMENT: 2 ten-sided dice or 2 twelve-sided dice

GETTING STARTED: At the same time each player rolls one die. Players must multiply the two numbers. The first player to say the correct product out loud scores one point. In the event of a tie, no one scores a point. Play continues for a set period of time or until a certain number of points have been reached.

FIGURE IT

SKILLS: multiplying three factors

PLAYERS: 2 - 4

EQUIPMENT: 2 twenty-sided dice, 1 ten-sided die, paper, pencil

GETTING STARTED: One player rolls the twenty-sided dice. Players multiply these two numbers to get a product. The same player rolls the ten-sided die. Players multiply this number with the previous product. The first player to call out the correct answer scores a point.

EXAMPLE: Roll 1:   20 and 15; 20 x 15 = 300

Roll 2:   7; 7 x 300 = 2100

Players alternate rolling the dice. Play continues until one player scores twenty points. Players may use pencil and paper or a calculator for their calculations.

VARIATION: All players that get the correct answer score a point.

MULTI BREAKER

SKILLS: multiplying to 144

PLAYERS: 2

EQUIPMENT: 2 twelve-sided dice per player

GETTING STARTED: Each player rolls their dice and multiplies the two numbers together. The player with the greatest product receives two points.

EXAMPLE:

Player 1	Player 2
9 x 7 = 63	4 x 8 = 32

Player one receives two points.

In the event of a tie (both players have the same product), a tie breaker must be played. Each player rolls the dice again to get a new product. The first player to roll a product greater than the "tie" wins four points.

EXAMPLE:

Player 1	Player 2
4 x 9 = 36	3 x 12 = 36

Tie "36"

Tie Breaker

5 x 5 = 25	7 x 6 = 42

Player two receives four points.

Play continues until one player scores fifty points.

MULTIPLICATION SCRAMBLE

SKILLS: recall of multiplication facts to 144

PLAYERS: 2 or solitaire

EQUIPMENT: 2 twelve-sided dice per player, gameboard, paper, pencil

GETTING STARTED: Each player makes a gameboard on their paper as follows (see appendix for reproducible page):

0 - 9	_____
10 - 19	_____
20 - 29	_____
30 - 39	_____
40 - 49	_____
50 - 59	_____
60 - 69	_____
70 - 79	_____
80 - 89	_____
90 - 99	_____
100 - 109	_____
110 - 119	_____
120 - 129	_____
130 - 139	_____
140 - 149	_____

The goal of the game is to fill in every line on the gameboard. Each player rolls two dice and multiplies them together. Players write down their products on the appropriate lines on their gameboards (ie. 4 x 7 = 28 would go on the line beside 20 - 29). The first player to get all lines on their gameboard filled is the winner.

EXAMPLE:

	Player 1	Player 2
0 - 9		
10 - 19		
20 - 29	28	
30 - 39	36	30
40 - 49	45	48
50 - 59		
60 - 69		
70 - 79		
80 - 89		
90 - 99		90
100 - 109		
110 - 119		
120 - 129		
130 - 139		
140 - 149		

Turn 1: Player one rolls 4 and 7 (4 x 7 = 28)

Turn 2: Player two rolls 5 and 6 (5 x 6 = 30)

VARIATION: To work on multiplication facts to 100, use two ten-sided dice per player. Use a gameboard up to 100 - 109.

THE BIG ROUND UP

SKILLS:	multiplying to 144, rounding off to nearest 10
PLAYERS:	2
EQUIPMENT:	2 twelve-sided dice, paper, pencil, gameboard
GETTING STARTED:	Each player creates a gameboard as follows: (see appendix for reproducible page)

10   20   30   40   50   60   70   80   90   100   110   120   130   140

The goal of the game is for players to cross off all the numbers on their gameboard. The first player to do so is the winner. Player one rolls the dice and multiplies them. The product is then rounded off to the nearest ten.

EXAMPLE:	Roll 6 and 12, 6 x 12 = 72 Round off to nearest ten = 70 Player crosses 70 off of their gameboard

Player two may then take their turn. Players alternate rolls, crossing numbers off their gameboards. If a player cannot cross off a number, play simply continues to the next player. The first player to cross off all of their numbers is the winner.

VARIATION:	When doubles are rolled, an extra turn is taken.

A ROUND OF DICE

SKILLS: multiplying four factors, rounding off to nearest 100

PLAYERS: 1 or more

EQUIPMENT: 4 ten-sided dice, paper, pencil, gameboard

GETTING STARTED: Each player has their own gameboard. The goal of the game is for players to cross off all numbers on their board. The first player to do so is the winner. Player one rolls the dice, multiplies them and says the product out loud. This number is then rounded off to the nearest hundred and crossed off their gameboard.

EXAMPLE: 7 x 4 x 1 x 9 = 252, 300 is crossed off

0   100   200   ~~300~~   400   500   600   700

If that number has already been crossed off, that turn is complete. Player two may then take their turn. Players alternate rolls until one player has crossed all numbers off their gameboard.

ON TARGET

SKILLS: multiplying facts to 100

PLAYERS: 2

EQUIPMENT: 2 ten-sided dice, gameboard

GETTING STARTED: Players use one gameboard as follows: (see appendix for reproducible page).

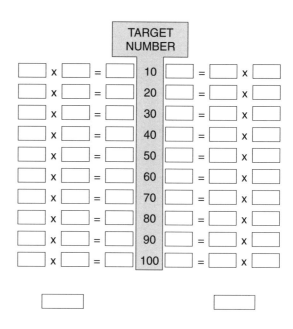

The goal of the game is for players to create a product as close to the Target Number without going over, on all ten lines. Player one rolls the die and decides where to put that number on their side of the gameboard. This number will be multiplied with another and the product compared to the Target Number at the completion of the rolls. Player two rolls the die and goes through the same procedure. Players continue to alternate turns until all spaces are filled in. THEN:

Players multiply their numbers and fill in the products. The products are compared to the Target Number. Whichever player has the closest number scores the point for that line. In the event of a tie (both products on a line are equal), both players score a point. Players compare their numbers to the Target Number on all ten lines and points are totalled. The player with the most points wins.

TANGLE WITH TWENTY

SKILLS: multi operations (+, −, x, ÷)

PLAYERS: 2 or teacher vs. whole class

EQUIPMENT: 2 ten-sided dice per player, pencil, gameboard

GETTING STARTED: Each player has two ten-sided dice and a gameboard (see appendix for reproducible page). The goal of the game is to cross off as many numbers as possible before getting three strikes. Player one rolls the dice. Player can +, -, x, or ÷ the two dice. Player can choose only one combination to take into their gameboard.

EXAMPLE: **Step 1**

player rolls 8 and 6 and possible combinations could include $8 + 6 = 14$
$$8 - 6 = 2$$

Player decides which combination they will take into their gameboard.

Step 2

Player chooses 14, and may now cross off two numbers that make that combination, such as 9 and 5 $(9 + 5 = 14)$, 2 and 7 $(2 \times 7 = 14)$, 18 and 4 $(18 - 4 = 14)$, etc.

0   1   2   3   4   5   6   7   8   9   10   11   12   13   14   15   16   17   18   19   20

X   X   X

Player two rolls the dice and follows the same procedure on their own gameboard. If a player cannot cross off any combination of numbers to match their roll they receive a strike, circling the X. After a player gets three strikes they stop rolling and wait until their opponent can no longer roll. Players compare their gameboards to see who crossed off the most numbers. The player with the most numbers crossed off is the winner. In the event of a tie, players can calculate the sum of their open numbers. The smallest sum wins.

VARIATION: Add another ten-sided die and cross off up to three numbers at a time.

FILL 'ER UP

SKILLS: adding, subtracting, collecting and organizing data in a bar graph, writing number sentences

PLAYERS: 2

EQUIPMENT: 1 twelve-sided die, 1 twenty-sided die, gameboard

GETTING STARTED: Each player has a gameboard (see appendix for reproducible page). The goal is to either fill in a column vertically or horizontally before the other player. Player one rolls the dice and can decide whether to add or subtract the numbers. Player records this number sentence in the appropriate space. Player two rolls the dice, adds or subtracts, and records the number sentence in the appropriate space. Players continue to alternate turns until one player fills in all numbers 0 - 30 horizontally or fills a vertical column with 15 combinations of one number.

EXAMPLE:

1	2	3	4	5	6	7	8	9	10	11	12	13	14	15	16	17	18	19	20	21	22	23	24	25	26	27	28	29	30
4-3			2+2					6+3 4+5 20-11	8+2			6+7	7+7	20-6	20-4 9+7				11+9										20+10

VARIATION: If a player rolls a double an additional roll may be taken. Players could multiply and divide the numbers rolled.

OR:

Fill in addition, subtraction for each roll AND if possible fill in multiplication and division combinations.

44

HIDE AND SEEK

SKILLS: graphing

PLAYERS: 2

EQUIPMENT: 2 twelve-sided dice per player, 1 graph per player (12 x 12)

GETTING STARTED: Each player has a 12 x 12 gameboard (see appendix for reproducible page) and hides ten points (o) on their graph. Player one rolls the dice and calls them out as coordinates (player chooses which way to call them, ie. either [2,3] or [3,2]). Player two checks his graph and calls "found" or "seek". Player one records the find or seek on their own graph grid. If it is a "found", player takes another turn. Players alternate turns until one player finds all of the other player's hidden points.

EXAMPLE:

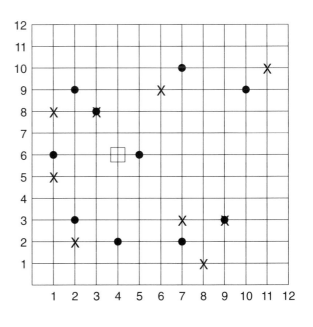

● hidden coordinates   X seek   ☐ found

TARGET THREE

SKILLS: graphing

PLAYERS: 2

EQUIPMENT: 2 ten-sided dice per player, gameboard

GETTING STARTED: Players use one gameboard as follows: (see appendix for reproducible page)

One player is 'X', the other is 'O'. The goal of this game is to get three coordinates in a row; either horizontally, vertically or diagonally. Player 'X' rolls the dice, identifies the coordinates, locates it on the gameboard and marks it by placing an 'X' (player chooses what order to call the rolls, ie. either (2,5) or (5,2)). Player 'O' then rolls the dice, identifies the coordinates, locates the appropriate place on the gameboard, and marks the spot with an 'O'. Players alternate turns. If a player lands on a point with their own mark, the player takes another turn. If a player lands on a point occupied by another player, they score a point, circle the mark, and it is now out of play (ie. 6,2).

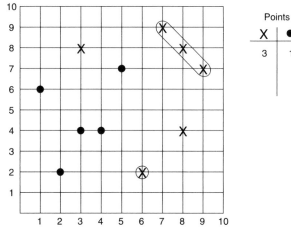

EXAMPLE: Player rolls 9 and 7 so coordinates can be either (9,7) or (7,9).
Player decides which would be more advantageous to their game and marks their gameboard.

When a player gets three coordinates in a row they are circled. Player scores three points. Play continues for a set period of time. The player with the most points is the winner.

46

THREE FOR ME

SKILLS: multiplying to 144

PLAYERS: 2

EQUIPMENT: multiplication table, 2 twelve-sided dice, bingo chips - two colors (or other markers), gameboard

GETTING STARTED: Players use one gameboard as follows: (see appendix for reproducible page)

Each player takes a color of bingo chips. Player one rolls the dice, multiplies them, and places their chips on possible combinations of that product.

EXAMPLE: Player rolls 6 and 4, places chip on combinations of 24, ie. 6,4 and 4,6 and 3,8 and 8,3 and 12,2 and 2,12

	1	2	3	4	5	6	7	8	9	10	11	12
1	1	2	3	4	5	6	7	8	9	10	11	12
2	2	4	6	8	10	12	14	16	18	20	22	(24)
3	3	6	9	12	15	18	21	(24)	27	30	33	36
4	4	8	12	16	20	(24)	28	32	36	40	44	48
5	5	10	15	20	25	30	35	40	45	50	55	60
6	6	12	18	(24)	30	36	42	48	54	60	66	72
7	7	14	21	28	35	42	49	56	63	70	77	84
8	8	16	(24)	32	40	48	56	64	72	80	88	96
9	9	18	27	36	45	54	63	72	81	90	99	108
10	10	20	30	40	50	60	70	80	90	100	110	120
11	11	22	33	44	55	66	77	88	99	110	121	132
12	12	(24)	36	48	60	72	84	96	108	120	132	144

Player verbalizes that their turn is over. Player two may then cover any missed combinations with their bingo chips. Player two then rolls 7 and 12 and puts a chip on combinations of 84.

Players alternate rolling the dice and placing chips on the board. The goal is for players to get three chips in a row either horizontally, vertically, or diagonally. If a player gets three in a row, they take them off the board and they become "keepers". They will be used at the end of the game to calculate the player's final score.

47

Stealing a Player's Chip: If a player rolls a number that is already occupied by the opposition, they can steal it. They take their opponent's chip and replace it with their own. The stolen chip is kept by the roller, and becomes a "keeper". It will be used at the end of the game to determine their final score.

Determining the Winner: After a set period of time the game ends. To determine the score, keepers are counted as follows:

Keepers of the player's own color = 2 points each
Keepers of the opponent's color = 5 points each
Own chips left on the board = 1 point each

The player with the most points wins.

1000 BULLSEYE

SKILLS:	adding to 20, multiplying to 100
PLAYERS:	2 or solitaire
EQUIPMENT:	2 ten-sided dice, paper, pencil
GETTING STARTED:	The goal of the game is to be the first player to reach 1000 exactly. Each player in turn rolls the dice. Players may either add them together to get a sum or multiply them to get a product. Player one rolls the dice and records their choice of sum or product. Player two then takes a turn and records their sum or product. Players keep alternating turns keeping a running total. Players may take a bonus roll if they hit a hundred exactly (ie. 100, 200, 300, etc.) or roll a double (ie. 2 and 2, 4 and 4, etc.). Strategy will come into play as players try to get bonus rolls by choosing a sum or product which would result in hitting a hundred exactly. Play continues until one player hits 1000 on the "bullseye."
VARIATION:	Solitaire: players can play individually. The number of rolls to 1000 can be calculated.

MULTI OPERATION BLACKOUT

SKILLS:	multi operations (+, -, x, ÷)
PLAYERS:	4: 2 teams of 2
EQUIPMENT:	2 hundreds boards, 3 ten-sided dice, bingo chips or other markers
GETTING STARTED:	The goal of the game is to be the first team to cover every number on their hundreds chart (see appendix for reproducible page). Team one rolls the three dice. Players figure out all of the combinations they can make with the three numbers using all operations.
EXAMPLE:	Roll 6, 9, 2

$$6 + 9 + 2 = 17$$
$$9 - 6 + 2 = 5$$
$$9 \times 6 + 2 = 56$$
$$6 \times 2 - 9 = 3$$
etc.

Player may cover up numbers 17, 5, 56, 3, etc.

For each answer, each team may cover that number on their hundreds chart. Teams are allowed a maximum of three minutes per roll. Team two then rolls the three dice and repeats the same procedure. Teams alternate turns until one team successfully covers up all of their numbers.

Note: Players could keep a written record of their rolls and multi operation sequences.

VARIATION:	At the end of a team's time limit the opposing team can "steal" any number combinations that their opponents have missed (ie. in above example team one misses 56. Team two covers 56 on their gameboard as a steal).
VARIATION:	Use 20-sided dice.

TARGET SUM

SKILLS: mixed operations (+, -, x, ÷)

PLAYERS: group of 5

EQUIPMENT: 5 twelve-sided dice per player, paper, pencil

GETTING STARTED: Each player rolls one die. These rolls are added to get a Target Sum for the group.

ie. $2 + 4 + 8 + 9 + 9$
Target Sum for group = 32

The goal for each player is then to roll their five dice and reach the Target Sum (32 in this example). Players may do this using any combination of operations (+, -, x, ÷). All numbers a player rolls must be used. Each player can score a point per round if they can reach the Target Sum with their numbers. After the round, players start again by each rolling one die and establishing a new Target Sum. Players then re-roll their five dice and try to reach the new Target Sum. The game ends after a set period of time. The player with the most points wins.

Bonus Points: If a group can create more than one sentence to hit the target sum, they score an extra point.

VARIATION: The class can be divided into groups and compete against one another. The teacher can roll the Target Sum. Each group rolls five dice and works together to try to reach the Target Sum. After a set number of rounds, groups total their points. The group with the most points is the winner.

SPEEDY GRAPHING

SKILLS: multi operations (+, -, x, ÷)

PLAYERS: 4: 2 vs. 2

EQUIPMENT: two ten-sided dice, gameboard, pencil

GETTING STARTED: Each team shares two ten-sided dice and one game-board (see appendix for reproducible page). When one person says "Go" all teams begin to roll their dice. Players may fill in up to four squares on their gameboard that equal a combination of the numbers rolled. For example, 3 and 6 are rolled. Players may color in a 9 square (3 + 6), a 3 square (6 - 3), an 18 square (6 x 3), and a 2 square (6 ÷ 3). Each team continues to roll and fill in their gameboard as quickly as possible. The first team of players to fill in one whole row of squares vertically or horizontally on their gameboard, wins.

VARIATION: Players write the equations in the appropriate squares.

" Dear Joanne, Jane & Cheryl,

I liked your presentation. I learned lots of fun games to play. You guys are terrific. Other kids would like to learn and play those games. I'm waiting for your next book to come out. I'm excited to read it. Thanks for coming. **"**

from L.K.
Grade 4

Reproducibles

ROLLING ALONG

1   2   3   4   5   6   7   8   9   10   11   12
                        X X X

1   2   3   4   5   6   7   8   9   10   11   12
                        X X X

1   2   3   4   5   6   7   8   9   10   11   12
                     X X X

1   2   3   4   5   6   7   8   9   10   11   12
                     X X X

1   2   3   4   5   6   7   8   9   10   11   12
                     X X X

1   2   3   4   5   6   7   8   9   10   11   12
                     X X X

1   2   3   4   5   6   7   8   9   10   11   12
                     X X X

ROLL IT AND MARK IT

1	2	3	4	5	6	7	8	9	10	11	12

1	2	3	4	5	6	7	8	9	10	11	12

1	2	3	4	5	6	7	8	9	10	11	12

SUBTRACT-A-GRAPH

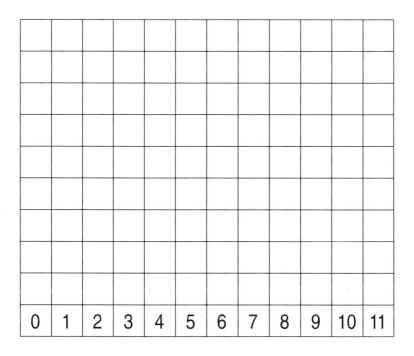

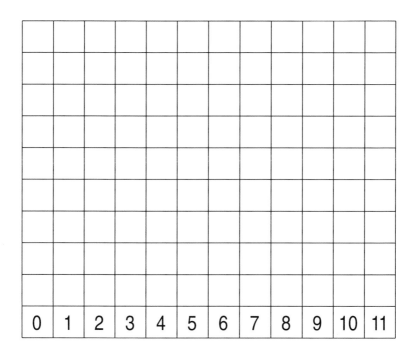

TIME OUT

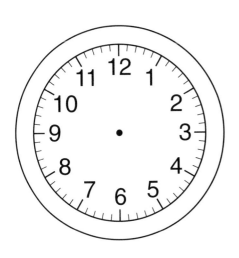
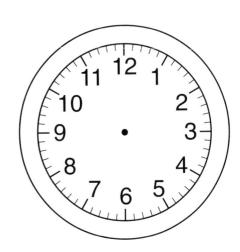
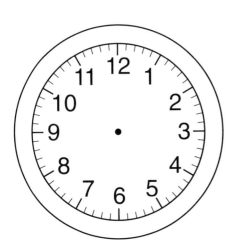
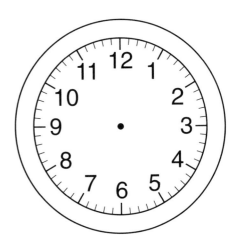

SUB TRACK

0	1	2	3	4	5	6	7	8	9	10	11
					X	X X					

0	1	2	3	4	5	6	7	8	9	10	11
					X	X X					

0	1	2	3	4	5	6	7	8	9	10	11
					X	X X					

0	1	2	3	4	5	6	7	8	9	10	11
					X	X X					

0	1	2	3	4	5	6	7	8	9	10	11
					X	X X					

0	1	2	3	4	5	6	7	8	9	10	11
					X	X X					

0	1	2	3	4	5	6	7	8	9	10	11
					X	X X					

WINNING TRACK CHALLENGER

```
0    1    2    3    4    5    6    7    8    9   10   11   12
                              X  X  X
```

```
0    1    2    3    4    5    6    7    8    9   10   11   12
                              X  X  X
```

```
0    1    2    3    4    5    6    7    8    9   10   11   12
                           X  X  X
```

```
0    1    2    3    4    5    6    7    8    9   10   11   12
                           X  X  X
```

```
0    1    2    3    4    5    6    7    8    9   10   11   12
                           X  X  X
```

```
0    1    2    3    4    5    6    7    8    9   10   11   12
                           X  X  X
```

```
0    1    2    3    4    5    6    7    8    9   10   11   12
                           X  X  X
```

MULTIPLICATION SCRAMBLE

0 - 9	_____	0 - 9	_____
10 - 19	_____	10 - 19	_____
20 - 29	_____	20 - 29	_____
30 - 39	_____	30 - 39	_____
40 - 49	_____	40 - 49	_____
50 - 59	_____	50 - 59	_____
60 - 69	_____	60 - 69	_____
70 - 79	_____	70 - 79	_____
80 - 89	_____	80 - 89	_____
90 - 99	_____	90 - 99	_____
100 - 109	_____	100 - 109	_____
110 - 119	_____	110 - 119	_____
120 - 129	_____	120 - 129	_____
130 - 139	_____	130 - 139	_____
140 - 149	_____	140 - 149	_____

0 - 9	_____	0 - 9	_____
10 - 19	_____	10 - 19	_____
20 - 29	_____	20 - 29	_____
30 - 39	_____	30 - 39	_____
40 - 49	_____	40 - 49	_____
50 - 59	_____	50 - 59	_____
60 - 69	_____	60 - 69	_____
70 - 79	_____	70 - 79	_____
80 - 89	_____	80 - 89	_____
90 - 99	_____	90 - 99	_____
100 - 109	_____	100 - 109	_____
110 - 119	_____	110 - 119	_____
120 - 129	_____	120 - 129	_____
130 - 139	_____	130 - 139	_____
140 - 149	_____	140 - 149	_____

THE BIG ROUND UP

10 20 30 40 50 60 70 80 90 100 110 120 130 140

10 20 30 40 50 60 70 80 90 100 110 120 130 140

10 20 30 40 50 60 70 80 90 100 110 120 130 140

10 20 30 40 50 60 70 80 90 100 110 120 130 140

10 20 30 40 50 60 70 80 90 100 110 120 130 140

10 20 30 40 50 60 70 80 90 100 110 120 130 140

10 20 30 40 50 60 70 80 90 100 110 120 130 140

10 20 30 40 50 60 70 80 90 100 110 120 130 140

10 20 30 40 50 60 70 80 90 100 110 120 130 140

10 20 30 40 50 60 70 80 90 100 110 120 130 140

ON TARGET

TARGET NUMBER

☐	x ☐	= ☐	10	☐	= ☐	x ☐	
☐	x ☐	= ☐	20	☐	= ☐	x ☐	
☐	x ☐	= ☐	30	☐	= ☐	x ☐	
☐	x ☐	= ☐	40	☐	= ☐	x ☐	
☐	x ☐	= ☐	50	☐	= ☐	x ☐	
☐	x ☐	= ☐	60	☐	= ☐	x ☐	
☐	x ☐	= ☐	70	☐	= ☐	x ☐	
☐	x ☐	= ☐	80	☐	= ☐	x ☐	
☐	x ☐	= ☐	90	☐	= ☐	x ☐	
☐	x ☐	= ☐	100	☐	= ☐	x ☐	

TANGLE WITH TWENTY

0 1 2 3 4 5 6 7 8 9 10 11 12 13 14 15 16 17 18 19 20
                        X X X

0 1 2 3 4 5 6 7 8 9 10 11 12 13 14 15 16 17 18 19 20
                        X X X

0 1 2 3 4 5 6 7 8 9 10 11 12 13 14 15 16 17 18 19 20
                        X X X

0 1 2 3 4 5 6 7 8 9 10 11 12 13 14 15 16 17 18 19 20
                        X X X

0 1 2 3 4 5 6 7 8 9 10 11 12 13 14 15 16 17 18 19 20
                        X X X

0 1 2 3 4 5 6 7 8 9 10 11 12 13 14 15 16 17 18 19 20
                        X X X

0 1 2 3 4 5 6 7 8 9 10 11 12 13 14 15 16 17 18 19 20
                        X X X

FILL 'ER UP

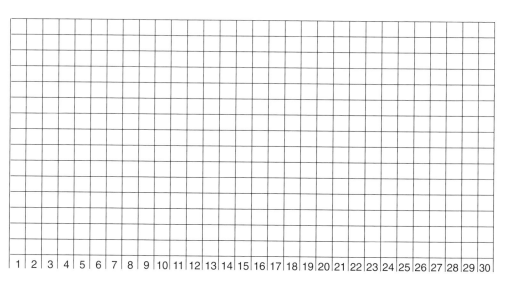

1 2 3 4 5 6 7 8 9 10 11 12 13 14 15 16 17 18 19 20 21 22 23 24 25 26 27 28 29 30

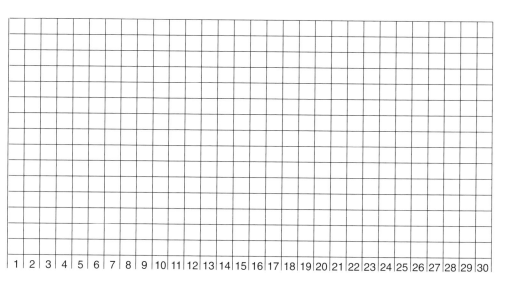

1 2 3 4 5 6 7 8 9 10 11 12 13 14 15 16 17 18 19 20 21 22 23 24 25 26 27 28 29 30

HIDE AND SEEK

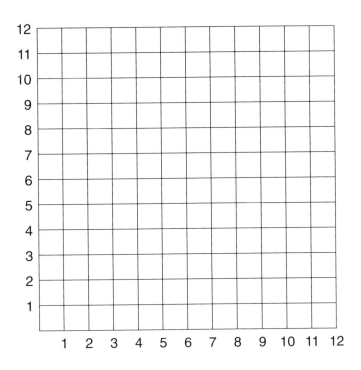

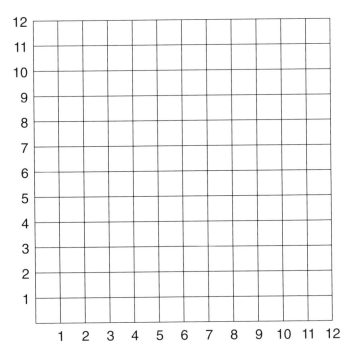

TARGET THREE

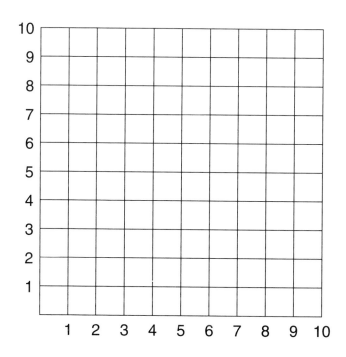

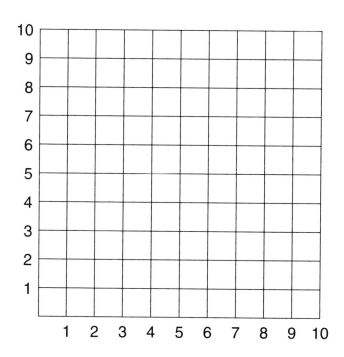

THREE FOR ME

	1	2	3	4	5	6	7	8	9	10	11	12
1	1	2	3	4	5	6	7	8	9	10	11	12
2	2	4	6	8	10	12	14	16	18	20	22	24
3	3	6	9	12	15	18	21	24	27	30	33	36
4	4	8	12	16	20	24	28	32	36	40	44	48
5	5	10	15	20	25	30	35	40	45	50	55	60
6	6	12	18	24	30	36	42	48	54	60	66	72
7	7	14	21	28	35	42	49	56	63	70	77	84
8	8	16	24	32	40	48	56	64	72	80	88	96
9	9	18	27	36	45	54	63	72	81	90	99	108
10	10	20	30	40	50	60	70	80	90	100	110	120
11	11	22	33	44	55	66	77	88	99	110	121	132
12	12	24	36	48	60	72	84	96	108	120	132	144

	1	2	3	4	5	6	7	8	9	10	11	12
1	1	2	3	4	5	6	7	8	9	10	11	12
2	2	4	6	8	10	12	14	16	18	20	22	24
3	3	6	9	12	15	18	21	24	27	30	33	36
4	4	8	12	16	20	24	28	32	36	40	44	48
5	5	10	15	20	25	30	35	40	45	50	55	60
6	6	12	18	24	30	36	42	48	54	60	66	72
7	7	14	21	28	35	42	49	56	63	70	77	84
8	8	16	24	32	40	48	56	64	72	80	88	96
9	9	18	27	36	45	54	63	72	81	90	99	108
10	10	20	30	40	50	60	70	80	90	100	110	120
11	11	22	33	44	55	66	77	88	99	110	121	132
12	12	24	36	48	60	72	84	96	108	120	132	144

THE HUNDRED BOARD

1	2	3	4	5	6	7	8	9	10
11	12	13	14	15	16	17	18	19	20
21	22	23	24	25	26	27	28	29	30
31	32	33	34	35	36	37	38	39	40
41	42	43	44	45	46	47	48	49	50
51	52	53	54	55	56	57	58	59	60
61	62	63	64	65	66	67	68	69	70
71	72	73	74	75	76	77	78	79	80
81	82	83	84	85	86	87	88	89	90
91	92	93	94	95	96	97	98	99	100

SPEEDY GRAPHING

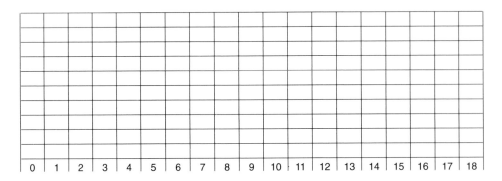

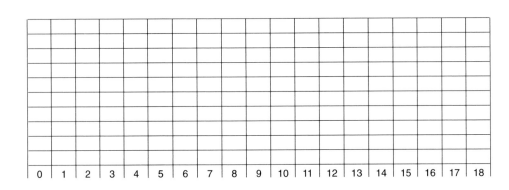

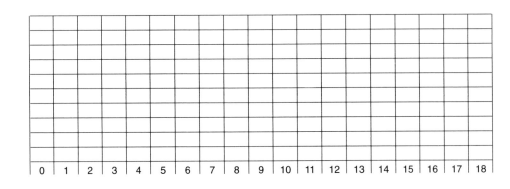